THE DINOSAUR COAST

Published by North York Moors National Park, 2001, on behalf of
the Yorkshire Dinosaur Coast Project

Reprinted 2002
Copyright © Roger Osborne 2001

North York Moors National Park
Information Service
The Old Vicarage
Bondgate
Helmsley
York YO62 5BP
Tel 01439 770657

A CIP catalogue record for this book is available from the
British Library

ISBN 0 907480 88 8

Designed by Alan Marshall

Printed and bound in Great Britain by Falcon Press,
Stockton-on-Tees

THE DINOSAUR COAST

YORKSHIRE ROCKS, REPTILES AND LANDSCAPE

Roger Osborne & Alistair Bowden

YORKSHIRE DINOSAUR
COAST PROJECT

Published by the North York Moors National Park
on behalf of the Yorkshire Dinosaur Coast Project

Contents

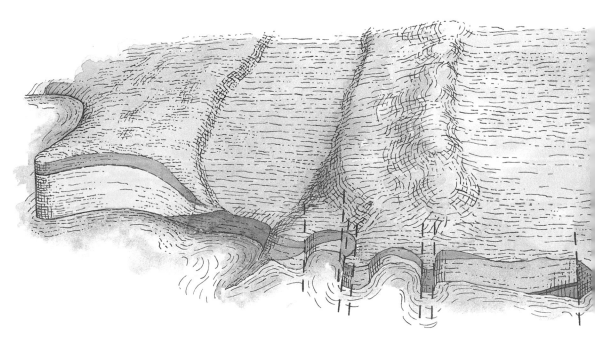

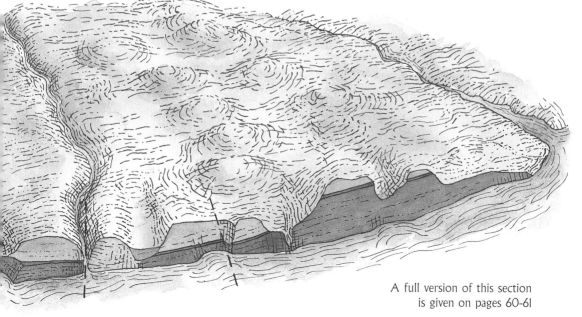

A full version of this section
is given on pages 60-61

WELCOME TO THE DINOSAUR COAST

From the mouth of the River Tees in the north, to Flamborough Head in the south, the Dinosaur Coast is one of the most spectacular and beautiful landscapes in England. The towering cliffs, rocky coves, massive headlands and sweeping bays are truly magnificent. And inland from the coast stretches an equally captivating land of high moors and forested hills, of dales and gorges, of escarpments and vales. This wonderful natural landscape has been enriched by the humans who have lived

Millions of years ago dinosaurs left their footprints on this coast.

here over thousands of years. The coastal towns and villages from Staithes to Whitby to Robin Hood's Bay to Scarborough and Filey have all been built with an understanding of the landscape. The heather moors and the breathtaking dales, with their checkerboards of green pastures and hedges and walls, have been created and sustained over generations by careful land management.

All this is immediately apparent to the human eye. But scratch the surface of this landscape and another story begins to appear. Pick up a pebble or, if you are lucky, a fossil off a beach, or run your hand along a cliff face and you are on the brink of entering another world. This world is all around us, we are separated from the age of dinosaurs by only one dimension – time. But by looking at our own world in a slightly different

way, we can cross the barrier of time. We can go back to an age when this area was under a great ocean full of strange shellfish and huge reptiles. Then we can see it change slowly to a coastline of deltas and forests and beaches. We can watch dinosaurs of all shapes and sizes leave their footprints in the mud and sand. Then the coast will change again to a shallow, warm, coral sea and then become clear, blue water, home to sponges and sharks. And, after all this time, when thousands of feet of sand and mud and lime and chalk have been laid down on the sea floor and squeezed into hard rock layers, we see the land lifted up so that the layers of rock form the cliffs of the coast. We then wind forward millions of years to look at the ice sheets and glacial lakes that put the final shape on the land. During this journey through time we see the different ways humans have used the land and what lies beneath it. Ironstone, harbours, agriculture, military defences, building stone, jet, alum, villages, towns, water supplies, shelter are all here because of the way this landscape is made.

All we need in order to enter this other world is a willingness to look around us and a little bit of guidance. So let this book be your guide and be ready to see and appreciate all the wonders of the Dinosaur Coast.

ANCIENT OCEAN

YORKSHIRE IN THE LOWER JURASSIC

Around 200 million years ago, at the beginning of the period we now call the Jurassic, this region was covered by sea. An extensive ocean covered the whole of Europe and was home to a great variety of marine life. Many of these creatures are preserved in the mudstones and thin limestones that were deposited on the ocean floor. Ammonites, belemnites and bivalves are common and occasionally we find the bones of one of the great marine reptiles — ichthyosaurs, plesiosaurs and crocodiles — that swam in these seas.

STAITHES and BOULBY

The northern part of the Dinosaur Coast is a dramatic seascape of towering cliffs and tiny coves. At Boulby the headland is over 200 metres high. The cliffs plunge vertically into the sea so human habitation is restricted to villages built into narrow gullies cut into the rock by streams. Both Staithes and Runswick Bay, with their jumbles of roofs and tiny twisting streets, are wonderfully picturesque but they were built that way out of necessity.

The cliffs at Boulby are among the highest in Britain. Gritty sandstones form the hard upper part of the cliffs. These are undercut as the softer, older mudstones that lie underneath are worn away by the sea. The hard rocks then break off and fall into the sea. The result is a series of immensely high vertical cliffs with just a small rock platform or scar at the foot, visible only at low tide.

 Lower Jurassic rocks

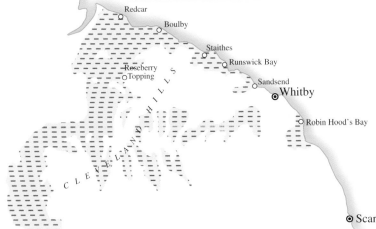

Rocks of the Lower Jurassic period, the oldest on the Yorkshire coast, lie on the surface along the coast north of Sandsend and in the low-lying country northwest of the Cleveland Hills. Further south natural erosion has worn away the harder younger rocks and the Lower Jurassic is exposed at Robin Hood's Bay, and in the dales of the North York Moors.

The combination of rock types and erosion works inland as well as on the coast. The steep northern escarpment of the Cleveland Hills is formed by erosion of the softer Lower Jurassic mudstones from underneath the hard Middle Jurassic grits that lie on top. The best-known example is Roseberry Topping, though here humans have speeded up the erosion by mining ironstone out of the side of the hill.

The village of Staithes is built in the ravine cut into the high cliffs by Staithes Beck. The high cliff to the west is Cowbar Nab. Good access to the sea is limited to the steep gullies at Staithes and Runswick Bay. Runswick has the only stretch of sand along this part of the coast.

The cliffs on this stretch of the coast are high and almost vertical because of their rock types. In the early part of the Jurassic period this region was a sub-tropical sea. Soft mudstones, shales and thin beds of limestone were laid on the sea bed. Later on, in the Middle Jurassic, the sea level fell and the area became a delta with coastal swamps. The rocks that were formed then were much harder sandy grits with thin layers of coal. All these rocks were lifted up several million years ago to lie in the great horizontal stacks we can see on the cliff faces. Harder rock sitting on top of soft rock has a striking effect on the landscape, giving steep escarpments and precipitous cliffs.

PLACES TO GO

■ The cliff top at **Boulby** is the site of an old alum works. From here there are dramatic views of the northern coast.

■ Lower Jurassic strata are beautifully displayed on the sea cliff of **Cowbar Nab** at **Staithes**.

■ **Roseberry Topping** and the northern face of the **Cleveland Hills** are among the great sights of the region. They can be seen from almost anywhere on the northwest margin of the North York Moors and are a welcome landmark to travellers from the south.

■ The Romans built signal stations on the cliff tops. Some remains can still be seen at **Huntcliff** south of **Saltburn** and near **Goldsborough**.

HUMMERSEA and AMMONITES

The rocks of the Yorkshire coast are famous for their fossils and above all for their ammonites. These coiled shells imprinted in rock have always been treasured for their strange beauty. Once geology developed into a science, it was realised that ammonites also had great importance as indicators of time. And it was here on the Dinosaur Coast that pioneers in the subject made discoveries about how fossils can unlock the secrets of the earth's history.

Dactylioceras, Lower Jurassic, Whitby (3 cm).

Perisphinctes, Upper Jurassic, Crossgates (45 cm).

Ammonites come in all sizes and varieties, which makes them very useful to geologists. The largest specimen here is a Perisphinctes from Upper Jurassic rocks at Crossgates, measuring 45 cm. The others are all from the Lower Jurassic; Hildoceras, Harpoceras and Dactylioceras, all from the Whitby area.

By the start of the Jurassic period, when the rocks of this area were beginning to be deposited in shallow seas, ammonites were one of the most common shelled sea creatures. They had survived a great extinction of marine life that happened 50 million years earlier and had flourished in the absence of many of their competitors. They diversified into different species and their shells took on a host of different forms. The ammonites died out in the next great extinction at the end of the Cretaceous period, along with the dinosaurs.

Ammonites are useful to geologists because, during the period when they flourished, they changed shape through time as some species died out to be replaced by others. Certain species are known to occur as fossils in just one layer of rock. If one of these species is widespread it can be used as a zone or index fossil. If you find a particular index fossil in a cliff-face at Whitby, and again in a rock at Staithes then you know you are looking at the same bed or stratum of rock. There is no need to trace the beds from one place to another, the index fossil does the work for you!

This section through an ammonite fossil shows the internal structure of its shell. The animal was like a modern-day squid and lived only in the outermost chamber. A thin tube connecting all the chambers was used to pump air in and out to control buoyancy.

A close relative of the ammonites, known as Nautilus, still survives in the Pacific Ocean.

Left, Hildoceras, Lower Jurassic, Whitby (14 cm)
Right, Harpoceras, Lower Jurassic, Whitby (10 cm)

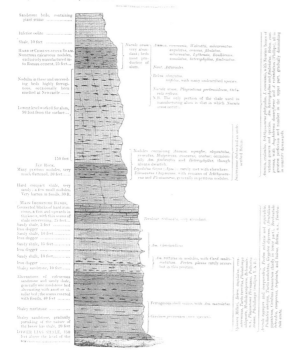

PLACES TO GO

■ There are ammonites of all kinds on display at **Whitby Museum** and at **Wood End** in **Scarborough**.
■ Fossil shops in Whitby and other towns have lots of specimens.
■ You can often find ammonite and other fossils in loose rock on the scars and beaches right along the coast. See the Fossil Hunting section on page 63 and never go near the base of the cliffs.

An amateur naturalist called Louis Hunton was born at Hummersea near Loftus in 1814. By carefully studying the cliffs near his home he realised that some fossils, particularly ammonite species, were restricted to certain beds. Hunton wrote a pioneering paper on how ammonites could be used as index fossils, which he presented to the Geological Society in 1836, when he was just twenty two years old. He drew a detailed section of the cliffs to illustrate his work (left). Two years later he died of tuberculosis. His grave is in the churchyard of St. Leonard's on Loftus High Street.

PORT MULGRAVE and IRONSTONE

Spend time walking around the villages and countryside of East Cleveland and the chances are you will come across some industrial relics. You might see a tunnel disappearing into a hillside, its entrance overgrown and blocked, or the remains of an old stone building or chimney, or even an iron grating covering a vertical shaft. These ghosts from the past are the remains of the Cleveland iron industry — in its heyday the most important source of iron and steel in Britain.

The discovery of iron ore in the Eston Hills near Guisborough in 1850 completely changed the economy of the region. Until then iron-making in the north was centred on small works in Durham and the Tyne valley. Within a few years mines were opened across East Cleveland and iron and then steel furnaces sprang up in Middlesbrough. The Teesside industrial complex was born.

The Dogger seam was mined on the east and west sides of Rosedale. Ore and coal were tipped directly into these kilns from the mines above. The resulting calcined ore was put in wagons on the railway.

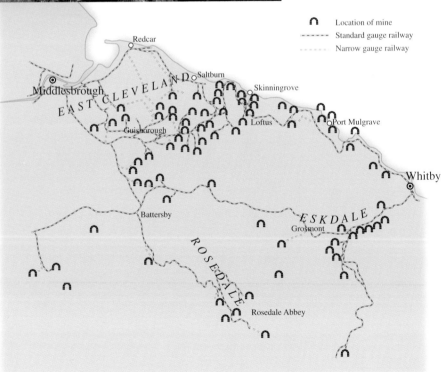

∩	Location of mine
------	Standard gauge railway
------	Narrow gauge railway

Redcar

Middlesbrough

EAST CLEVELAND

Saltburn

Skinningrove

Guisborough

Loftus

Port Mulgrave

Whitby

Battersby

ESKDALE

Grosmont

ROSEDALE

Rosedale Abbey

Ironstone works were generally drift mines, so the mine entrances are where the seams break the surface. The Main seam was up to 3.5 metres thick and was worked in East Cleveland and down the coast, while the thinner Pecten and Avicula seams were worked around Grosmont in Eskdale. All three lie in Lower Jurassic rocks. The Dogger seam marks the beginning of the Middle Jurassic and was worked principally at Rosedale. A vast network of railways fetched ore from the mine heads to furnaces at Middlesbrough and Redcar.

Loftus mine workers at the entrance to the pit in 1903. The East Cleveland ironstone industry was in its heyday from 1850 to about 1912. Some pits carried on working until the 1960s.

Stone jetties and an artificial harbour lie at the foot of steep cliffs in an isolated spot between Staithes and Runswick Bay. This is Port Mulgrave, built by the Grinkle Iron Mining Company. This outfit was owned by Palmers of Jarrow and the harbour was built to ship ore to their blast furnaces on the Tyne. But why build at the foot of a cliff and how was the ore to be brought down to the boats? The answer lies in an inclined tunnel, built down from mines inland at Borrowby Dale (near the Fox and Hounds pub) to the foot of the cliff. The tunnel entrance is still visible at Port Mulgrave, and the Ship Inn at the cliff top has a painting showing trains of ore tubs emerging from the tunnel mouth, shooting ore into the holds of steamers. Now the harbour is home to a few small fishing boats.

For the iron mines near the coast, boats were the obvious way to transport the ore to Middlesbrough. But the high cliffs made this nearly impossible between Skinningrove and Sandsend. One mining company solved the problem by building its own harbour which it grandly named Port Mulgrave.

PLACES TO GO

■ Take a tour of an old ironstone mine at the **Tom Leonard Mining Museum** at **Skinningrove**. The staff know everything there is to know about the Cleveland iron industry and the shop is full of books, photographs and leaflets. Notice the red colour of the stones on Skinningrove beach stained by iron – there was a legend among sailors that shipwrecks along the coast were common, because there was so much iron in the rocks that ships' compasses were deflected!

■ The Skinningrove steel works is still in operation in the next-door village of **Carlin How**. Steel is still being processed on Teesside at the Corus plant near **Redcar**.

■ You can walk down the steep path to the foot of the cliff at **Port Mulgrave**. The jetties are still there as is the tunnel entrance.

■ The old railway track round **Rosedale** gives easy walking past the ironstone kilns and wonderful views down the dale towards the Vale of Pickering.

KETTLENESS and the SEA MONSTERS

The headland at Kettleness, jutting out into the North Sea, is a wild and beautiful place. The views to the northwest across Runswick Bay and southeast towards Whitby are spectacular. But look down and you will see something very strange – a bare 'moonscape' of loose grey shale, 20 metres below your feet. This desolate spot is a huge abandoned alum quarry, and this is where the remains of great marine reptiles, the biggest fossils found on the Yorkshire coast, have been discovered.

Marine reptiles – plesiosaurs, ichthyosaurs and crocodiles – swam in the shallow seas of the Lower Jurassic period. When they died their remains were preserved in the soft shales that were being formed on the sea bed. The shales were lifted up to form part of the landmass of Britain but the fossilised bones lay undisturbed for more than 180 million years. Then, in the 1600s, the shales were found to be the source of a valuable chemical called alum (for more on alum see page 26). As the shale was dug out of the cliffs, thousands of different types of fossils were discovered. In the 1800s people began to understand that these were scientifically and commercially valuable and so they were preserved. The most spectacular finds were the fossilised bones of the great sea reptiles, often between 3 and 6 metres in length. Fortunately some of these were bought by local museums and are still on display.

From above, the old quarry at Kettleness is like a bare shelf sticking out into the sea (left). No plants have grown on the piles of loose shale left over from the alum-making, giving the landscape a forbidding look. From Runswick Bay (above) you can see how the headland has been scooped out by the quarry-men. More marine reptiles have been found here than at almost any other location on the Yorkshire coast. Now that quarrying has stopped, finds are much less common, though a complete ichthyosaur skeleton was found here in 1999 by sharp-eyed palaeontologist Brian Foster.

This skull of a marine crocodile is in Wood End Museum, Scarborough.

The largest reptile fossil ever found on the Dinosaur Coast is this plesiosaur, Rhomaleosaurus cramptoni. It was unearthed at Kettleness alum quarry in 1848. The fossil is now in storage in the National Museum of Ireland but a beautiful cast is on display in the Natural History Museum in London.

Plesiosaurs had broad bodies with large paddles. Their necks were often long and slender. Cartoons of the Loch Ness monster look very like plesiosaurs! Ichthyosaurs were more fish-shaped (the name means fish-lizard) resembling a present-day dolphin.

PLACES TO GO

■ Access to the old quarries at **Kettleness** is via a steep and difficult cliff path. It is better to view the site from the Cleveland Way cliff top path.
■ From **Runswick Bay** look across to see the missing part of the headland.
■ The same effect can be seen at Sandsend. Look north from the beach to see how the cliff at **Sandsend Ness** has been demolished. The cliff path goes through the quarries and heaps of spoil.
■ Reptile fossils are on display at **Whitby Museum**. Further afield, visit the **Yorkshire Museum** in York and the **Natural History Museum** in London to see some more Yorkshire reptiles.

WHITBY MUSEUM

Wonderful sights on the Yorkshire coast are not restricted to the great outdoors. If you want to see giant reptiles, ammonites as big as a barrel and a thousand other rocks and fossils – as well as Captain Cook, a hundred different ships, fabulous jet ornaments, costumes and weapons from the South Seas, remains from the Romans to the Victorians, the famous Hand of Glory, and a multitude of other treasures, then Whitby Museum is the place to visit.

Just walking along the quayside and through the narrow streets, you sense that Whitby's history is all around you. And what a history! From fishing, to religion, poetry, ship-building, whaling, exploration, coastal trading, geology, shipwrecks, alum and jet; it is doubtful whether there is a small town in the world that can match Whitby's past for sheer variety and fascination. The exuberance of this past is captured in the wonders of Whitby Museum.

Whitby Museum was founded in 1824. In the 1930s it moved from the quayside to Pannett Park. To get there walk from the western end of the swing bridge up the steep cobbled street, then up Flowergate. Pannett Park is on your left at the top. From here there are wonderful views across to the Abbey.

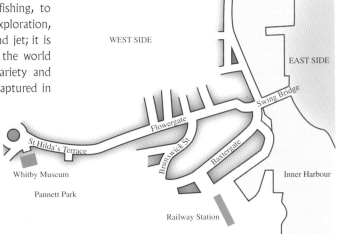

This is no ordinary museum. You will not find flashing lights and animated monsters from TV shows. Instead, when you enter the museum, you enter another world. With minor adjustments, the museum is as it was when it was moved to its present home in the 1930s. Successive generations have recognised the unique atmosphere of the place and have decided to preserve its magic. You might feel overwhelmed at first by the quantity and variety of treasures. Just relax and take your time – the museum rewards the patient visitor. And you can always come back; some people have made lots of visits and still see things they previously missed!

Giant ichthyosaurs and plesiosaurs found in the Whitby area are built into the museum's walls. Most of these were found by men quarrying for alum or jet, though there was a professional band of fossil hunters too – a good living could be made selling specimens to private collectors and museums.

Martin Simpson devoted much of his life to collecting and classifying fossils for the museum's collection. His 19th century books on the ammonites and other fossils of the Yorkshire coast formed the basis for much of our understanding of the Lower Jurassic period. He is remembered as a scientist of international importance.

The fossils are displayed as they were 70 years ago but these are a small proportion of the museum's world-famous collection. The specimens are stored in special acid-free boxes in a stable environment (above, right).

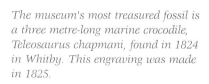

The museum's most treasured fossil is a three metre-long marine crocodile, *Teleosaurus chapmani*, found in 1824 in Whitby. This engraving was made in 1825.

WHITBY HARBOUR

Whitby is one of the glories of the British coast. The great abbey ruins tower over the tumble of streets, churches, shops, pubs and houses crowding between the cliff-tops and the harbour. From any vantage point Whitby and its harbour is a breath-taking sight. The harbour gave birth to the town — without the River Esk and its natural estuary the port of Whitby with its fishing, whaling, shipbuilding and coastal trading would never have existed. But the River Esk didn't always meet the sea at Whitby, and the reason it does is because of a geological fault.

The science of geology was in its infancy when local naturalists first noticed something strange about the cliffs at Whitby. On the east side of the harbour, under the abbey, the cliffs are very high with lots of thin beds of dark shales. On the west side the cliffs are much lower and are made of great blocks of yellow sandstone. As early as 1817 it was suggested that there must be a geological fault running through the harbour, and that the rocks on the west side had slipped downwards by as much as 100 feet. Although the line of the fault could not be seen because it ran along the river, later geologists all agreed, some estimating the downthrow of the fault at over 200 feet. Sixty years ago geologists made a startling discovery — the rocks on the east and west cliffs at Whitby are exactly the same age. But how could they be so different when they were formed at the same time? And was the Whitby fault an illusion?

The rocks on the west side at Whitby (left) are quite different from those on the east cliff (above) but they are the same age. When these rocks were deposited, around 180 million years ago, this area was a coastal swamp or delta. By studying modern deltas we can see that there are areas of swamp, full of dark stagnant mud, alongside channels made by flowing fresh water with beds of clean yellow sand. This is how the mismatch between the Whitby cliffs came about – the east side is the product of a swamp, the west side is the remnant of a channel. And what about the fault? We still think it is there, but with a downthrow of only a metre or so. That was probably enough to capture the waters of the Esk and bring it to Whitby. So, while it may not be so dramatic as we once thought, Whitby does, after all, owe its existence to a geological fault.

At the end of the last Ice Age, about 10,000 years ago, retreating ice sheets had dumped a great bank of mud along the coast. This blocked off all the rivers from flowing into the North Sea, including the Esk. The diverted waters flowed into a dip caused by the Whitby fault and cut the deep gorge we see today.

PLACES TO GO

■ The old Whitby lifeboat makes short trips out from the West Quay. Look back towards the town from the sea and you will notice the contrast between the cliffs on either side of the harbour.
■ The sandstone of the west cliffs can be seen in the cutting at Khyber Pass and from the west beach.
■ The east cliff, under the abbey, can be seen from the east breakwater. Look up and you will see that the thin beds of shale and mudstone are capped by a layer of paler and more yellow sandstone. When looking at cliffs, always beware of falling rocks.

Dislocation of Strata

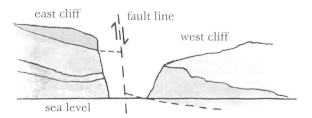

As well as being a wonderful example of how rocks can reveal the Earth's history, the Dinosaur Coast was a magnet for early geologists. George Young noted the fault at Whitby in 1817 then John Phillips in 1829 included this section (above, left) across the harbour in his survey of the geology of the coast. At the very top of the east cliff there is a bed of sandstone similar to the rocks of the west cliff. Phillips assumed that there had been a slip downwards on the west side, as shown above, right.

SALTWICK JET

For at least four thousand years people have treasured a strange, opaque, black stone called jet. But when the Victorians made jet an essential and enduring fashion item, the industry really took off and Whitby jet became known across the world. Although popular from earliest Victorian times, jet jewellery became

universal after 1861. Queen Victoria went into mourning following Prince Albert's death and only jet ornaments were allowed to be worn at court.

High infant mortality meant that many Victorian women spent long periods in mourning but they were still determined to be fashionable. Dark voluminous crinoline dresses became the rage. These needed large brooches and necklaces. Jet fitted the bill perfectly; it was black, extremely light and could be carved into elegant shapes. The jet found in the cliffs around Whitby was thought to be the highest quality, better than imported jet from France and Spain. The local industry thrived. But after Victoria's Golden Jubilee in 1887 fashions changed again. The Queen relaxed her mourning, smoother dresses in brighter colours came in — the jet industry never really recovered from the naughty nineties.

Jet is formed from the fossilised trunks of monkey puzzle or araucaria trees. In the Lower Jurassic period these trees grew in coastal swamps in this area (strangely enough this imported one is growing in a garden near Ruswarp). When the trees died they fell to the ground and formed a decaying layer. The hardest jet is thought to come from trees submerged in sea water.

Native jet often retains the shape and texture of the tree that made it. This 60 cm-long piece is preserved in Whitby Museum. Native jet is dull with a brown tinge, only when it is polished does it become a deep and lustrous black.

The Whitby jet industry began in earnest in the 1830s. At first there was enough jet picked up off the beaches but mining became necessary as the industry expanded. These old 'jet holes' are in the cliff at Sandsend. The mines are extremely dangerous and are entirely worked out.

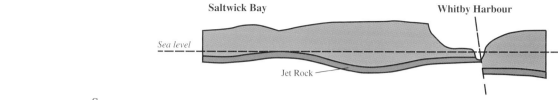

Saltwick Bay **Whitby Harbour**

Sea level

Jet Rock

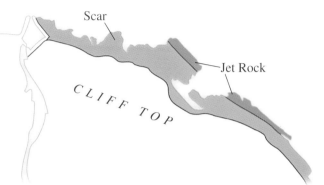

Scar

Jet Rock

C L I F F   T O P

The jet rock forms a seam about 7 metres thick that is exposed along the cliffs at several places from Saltburn to Sandsend and from Saltwick south to Ravenscar. The best jet was found in the top 3 metres of this layer. The nearest jet rock to Whitby is at Saltwick, just to the south. Here it lies at the base of the low water reef and is only visible at very low tides. The seam has been extensively worked out.

PLACES TO GO

■ You can see evidence of jet workings to the north of Sandsend.
■ Saltwick Nab, the headland at Saltwick Bay, was the nearest jet rock to Whitby itself.
■ Whitby Museum has a fine display of jet jewellery and ornaments as well as some native jet.
■ Jet is still being carved to make jewellery for sale in several shops on Whitby's East Side.

The Jet Miners Inn at Great Broughton is evidence of inland jet mining. The seams on the coastal cliffs were dangerous to work, so miners took to tunnelling into the Lower Jurassic rock inland. The jet seam was worked around Great Ayton, through Bilsdale, around Swainby and Osmotherley, and at Bransdale and Rosedale, as well as on the coast.

This carved jet bracelet is on display in Whitby Museum. Although Victorian designs dominate, jet has enjoyed a comeback in recent years, though there is no longer any jet mining.

ROBIN HOOD'S BAY

The great arc of Robin Hood's Bay is one of the most famous and beautiful sights on the Yorkshire coast, and the village is one of the most picturesque anywhere in England. The shape of the bay comes from the underlying rocks, and in particular from an odd structure that has bent the rock strata into long curves. It is these curves that make the bay, when seen from above, so remarkably graceful.

During the Tertiary period, long after the Jurassic rocks of this region had been deposited, the whole area was lifted up. This happened because two of the great plates that make up the earth's crust collided, making the earth's surface buckle and fold. The area buckled upwards, forming a long arch that runs from east to west across the high moors (see pages 60-61). Robin Hood's Bay is at the eastern end of this arch.

The village at Robin Hood's Bay is similar to Staithes and Runswick Bay because the underlying rock types are the same. Here too soft shales sit beneath harder younger grits. When the cap rocks are worn away steep gullies result.

At Robin Hood's Bay the long arch of rocks that forms the central plateau of the North York Moors reaches the sea. Here another geological feature forms the arc of the bay. Forces from different directions have pushed against the rock strata and made it buckle upwards into a dome. The dome is curved on all sides and lends its shape to the bay.

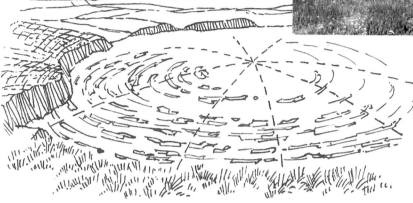

The sea has worn away a 'wave-cut platform' that reveals the underlying rock structure. If you measure the slope of the beds on the scar, and sketch where they were before they were worn away, you can see the shape of the dome.

The bay has long been a magnet for fossil collectors. There is no need to disturb the scar or the cliffs, there are always plenty of rocks lying on the shore. Ammonites are sometimes found in hard concretions that become separated from the rock. These have to be broken open, though most are simply solid rock. It's best just to keep your eyes peeled for fossils in recent cliff falls. The commonest ammonites found here are Dactylioceras. You might also find belemnites, though a slab like the one shown here is rare.

PLACES TO GO

■ The area around and above the bay is criss-crossed by paths all offering great walks and wonderful views. Try starting at **Ravenscar**. From here you can walk along **Stoupe Brow** or down to the beach.
■ There is easy access to the beach at **Boggle Hole**, situated half way round the bay. Make sure you are aware of the tides if you walk along the scar.
■ Robin Hood's Bay village is a delight at any time but it gets crowded on summer weekends. In the winter with a northeasterly wind driving a high sea you will appreciate the snugness of the cheek-by-jowl houses, and particularly the pubs and tea-rooms!

RAVENSCAR ALUM

All along the Dinosaur Coast, parts of the cliff are missing! You might expect the flat cliff-tops to extend outwards and then drop steeply towards the sea. Instead, at a host of different places, the cliff dips down on to a flat shelf, and then down to the sea. Seen from the side it looks as if a giant hand has scooped a great mass of rock out of the cliff – and this is exactly what has happened. Or, more exactly, men wielding spades and pick-axes have, over hundreds of years, moved millions of tons of shale from the cliffs of the Yorkshire coast: all in order to make a chemical that was vital to every trading economy – alum.

Alum is used as a fixative for dyes and as an agent in tanning leather. Textiles are an important industry today; in the pre-industrial age they were the lifeblood of European trade and prosperity. After the Reformation England lost its supplies of alum from Italy. In the six-teenth century woollen cloth products made up 80 per cent of English exports – without alum for dyeing the country would be in serious difficulties. After a few false starts a source rock for alum was discovered near Guisborough in the early 1600s. Quite soon the same rock was found along the cliffs of the coast between Loftus and Sandsend, at Saltwick and again around Robin Hood's Bay. Compare the map of alum sites (below) with the map on page 10 to see that the alum shale is of Lower Jurassic age.

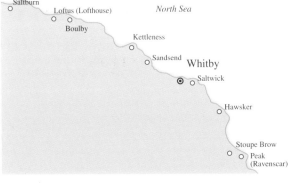

Alum shale is exposed in Lower Jurassic rocks along the coast and, occasionally, inland. The biggest works were on the coast because quarrying and transport were easier.

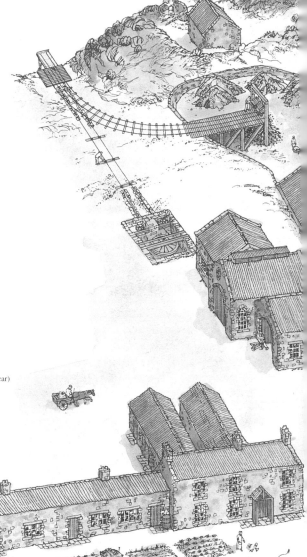

Nowadays Ravenscar is a tranquil spot. But when the alum works were in full swing, from 1650 to 1862, this was a hive of activity. The alum shale was hacked out of the escarpment up above and piled into great heaps on the quarry floor. These were burned (there was enough carbon in the shale to keep it cooking for months) until the shale separated into a red slag and a white powder. The powder was dissolved in water and sent down to the works in gullies. Once there, the liquid was repeatedly heated and cooled in order to get pure alum to crystallise out. The crystals were then packed in barrels and taken down the cliff on an inclined railway to the ships waiting below. The works employed 150 men who lived with their families in cottages near the alum works.

PLACES TO GO

■ The **Peak Alum Works** and quarries are easily accessible by footpath from Ravenscar. The works have been preserved by the National Trust and information boards on the site give a detailed history. The quarries are also the site of the old Ravenscar brick works.
■ You can see the quarries and spoil heaps looking north from **Sandsend**, and you can walk through them along the coastal path.
■ There are remnants of the alum industry at **Saltwick**, at **Kettleness** and at **Boulby**.

Millions of tons of shale were quarried to make alum. The effect on the landscape is most dramatic where the quarries were on the cliff face, as at Sandsend (above), Saltwick and Kettleness.

DELTAS AND FORESTS

YORKSHIRE IN THE MIDDLE JURASSIC

The ocean had receded from this area by the time of the Middle Jurassic, around 170 million years ago. This was now a coastal area of deltas and scrub and forest. The sea level varied through this period, occasionally submerging the coastal strip. The marine fossil sea shells we find in other periods are now joined by plant remains and the traces of land animals. Dinosaurs left their mark here in the form of footprints and the occasional bone. The rocks of this period are mostly sandstone and mudstone.

THE PEAK FAULT

At first sight the landscape of the Dinosaur Coast appears quite uniform – towering cliffs occasionally interrupted by small inlets or coves and, once in a while, a sweeping bay. But each section of the coast has its own story that marks it out as different from the rest. When we reach the headland known as the Peak, at the village of Ravenscar, we enter a different geological world. The boundary between the rocks to the northwest and those to the southeast is a gash in the earth's surface known as the Peak Fault.

The rocks to the south and east have dropped down the plane of the fault by about 150 metres, evidence of a catastrophic earth movement. This means the rocks that outcrop on the cliffface and clifftop are much younger to the south. Up to now, as we travel south we have seen hard Middle Jurassic rocks overlying softer older shales. The Peak headland has the last of the old Lower Jurassic rocks – from here to Filey the coast has alternating Middle and Upper Jurassic rocks, with a few miles of much more recent glacial mud cliffs thrown in. Much of this section of the coast is formed by a series of faults that push out the great headlands at Scarborough, Cayton and Filey Brigg and create the magnificent bays that fall in between.

The Peak Fault actually splits in two right at the headland, creating a narrow outcrop of Lower Jurassic sandstones down at beach level. The harder sandstone forms a reef known as the Peak Steel which extends 500 metres out from the headland. The earth movement that created such a large fault was massive. The Peak Fault is the most northerly and biggest of a series of faults that cross the coastline.

Scarborough Castle Hill, Osgodby Point, Red Cliff at Cayton are all created by faults bringing hard and soft rocks next to each other at the surface. The region between Ravenscar and Red Cliff has effectively dropped down between two fault systems. This kind of structure is quite common and is known as a graben. The most famous present-day one is the Great Rift Valley in East Africa, which is still dropping.

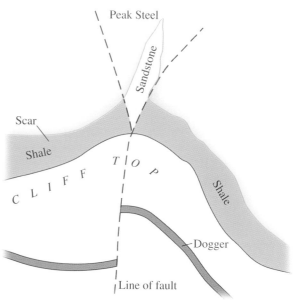

Half way down the path to the shore from Ravenscar, the line of the fault becomes clearly visible (above). The ends of these beds have been forced down by movement of the fault and end abruptly at the line of the fault which runs diagonally from top right to bottom left. The vegetation changes across this boundary with lots of gorse on the left and none to the right of the line – a sure sign of a change in the underlying rock types.

The Peak fault splits at the headland bringing a wedge of hard sandstone to the surface. As well as dropping to the southeast of the fault, the land has moved along it, displacing the Dogger bed by as much as 400 metres.

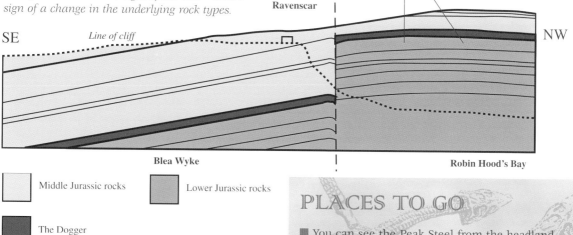

Middle Jurassic rocks

Lower Jurassic rocks

The Dogger

Because the rocks on the southeastern side of the fault have slipped downwards, younger rocks appear in the cliff face. The Dogger is the bottom (i.e. oldest) bed of the Middle Jurassic. The older rocks below this soon disappear to the southeast. In the hillside that arcs behind Robin Hood's Bay there are exposures of the three economic minerals of the Lower Jurassic – the Alum Shales, Jet Rock and Cleveland Ironstone.

PLACES TO GO

■ You can see the Peak Steel from the headland at **Ravenscar**.
■ It is possible to reach the shore via a footpath from Ravenscar. Visits to the shore at the headland should only be made on a falling tide. Be warned – it is a long steep climb back to the top.
■ Sudden boundaries of young and old rocks can produce striking effects on the landscape. You can see this at **Scarborough Castle Hill**, at both ends of **Cayton Bay** and at **Filey Brigg**.

JURASSIC JUNGLE

When dinosaurs roamed along the coast this was a changing landscape of deltas, beaches, mudbanks and sandbars. Rivers flowed down to a warm, shallow sea teeming with life. This was the period known as the Middle Jurassic. The coastal zone was an ideal place for plants and the fine silts and muds have proved to be excellent at preserving their delicate leaves and stems. These fossil plants have been avidly studied by scientists for over a century and the Jurassic flora of Yorkshire remains an important key to understanding the past.

Fossils help us to estimate the relative ages of rocks and they tell us about the evolution of organisms through time and space. But they also tell us about the conditions in which they lived. Because plants are particularly sensitive to climate and environmental conditions, they are extremely useful in telling us about this part of the world in the Middle Jurassic. All of the major plant groups that were alive in the northern hemisphere are represented in the fossils that have been found on the Yorkshire coast. Ferns, cycads, seed ferns and gingkos grew on the delta plain, while conifers probably thrived on the more upland areas. The climate was warm and humid, though growth rings on some tree stems show that this was a seasonal and therefore non-tropical, climate.

The oldest type of plant, in evolutionary terms, in Jurassic times were the seed-ferns. They are now extinct, though their descendant the cycad, which was also around in Jurassic times, still exists. The seedferns were small plants with broad stems topped by a series of palm-like leaves (above). Ferns covered the ground while tree ferns (right) grew on the delta plain and conifers (left) dominated the skyline. Flowering plants or angiosperms did not develop until after the Jurassic. Even though angiosperms are the dominant plants in today's world, and are the main plant food of mammals, conifers are still a hugely important group – they have been around for over 300 million years.

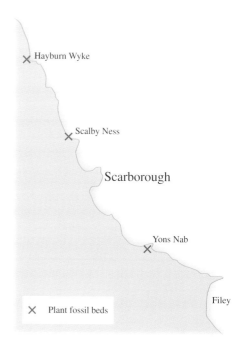

Plant fossils are found in several different rock groups within the Middle Jurassic rocks of the Yorkshire coast, showing that they were present here for a long period. The main plant fossil beds are at Hayburn Wyke, Scalby Ness and Yons Nab at Cayton Bay. One reason that scientists study the Yorkshire Jurassic flora is the diversity of plant material. Because they have been studied and classified so thoroughly in the past, present-day scientists find them particularly useful. The emphasis has changed from the classification of fossil plants towards using them to work out the relationships between different rock formations. It was the presence of plant fossils in the cliffs on either side of Whitby Harbour that showed the extent of the fault.

The Jurassic flora of Yorkshire is extremely diverse. The delicate structures are often very well preserved as in these drawings (above) and this specimen from Whitby Museum.

CLOUGHTON SANDSTONE

Many of the most beautiful sights of the coast, the moorland and the dales are the results of human interaction with the landscape. The hilltop forests, the heather moors and the lowland pastures are very picturesque. But humans have also used the landscape and its rocks in another way — as a source of building stone. The houses and churches and shops of the villages, and the stone walls of the field boundaries, seem to be a natural part of the landscape. The colours of the stone blend perfectly with the natural world — not surprising, since the stone was quarried from the surrounding hillsides.

There are a host of different rock types in northeast Yorkshire. Some, like ironstone and alum shale are useful for minerals; others like the volcanic rock of the Cleveland Dyke are good for roadstone or for setts; and some are ideal for building. Because stone is difficult to transport it is easiest to use the nearest supply. As you travel around the region you can see changes in the stone used for buildings. It is best to look at dry stone walls or cottages, since grand buildings sometimes did use stone from elsewhere. When labour was plentiful and manufacture expensive, local stone was the cheapest building material; now it is among the most expensive.

Quarries near Cloughton were a source of fine building sandstone. This stone is known as Moor Grit from the Middle Jurassic period. Sandstones are formed on seabeds and on beaches and sometimes, as at Cloughton, in rivers. The Moor Grit could easily be cut into regular squared blocks because of its consistent internal structure.

This house at Cloughton (above) is made from local sandstone. These regular, square blocks of yellow sandstone contrast with the irregular, narrow pieces of stone in the house at Ebberston (above, right). These are pieces of local oolitic limestone from the Tabular Hills. The limestone fractures into much narrower pieces than the Moor Grit. This farm at Mowthorpe in Forge Valley (below) has used gritstone for the house and limestone for the retaining walls. The soft chalk of the Wolds is not good for building so here, as in this cottage at Langtoft (right), brick has been used.

PLACES TO GO

■ Building stone is, of course, all around us. It is fascinating to note the changes in local stone use. See, for instance, the stone walls that border the main road at **Cloughton** and contrast them to the wall built alongside the A170 above **Ruston**.

■ Many of the older grand buildings in Scarborough are of stone – the **Crescent**, the **Art Gallery** and **Wood End** were all built in the 1830s and 1840s. By the 1860s brick was chosen for the **Grand Hotel** and then for the **Town Hall**. This might have been a deliberate display of wealth.

■ The chalk of the Wolds is unsuitable for building, so there is a sudden change to brick, even in old cottages. Some modern builders have begun to use flint, which is found in irregular nodules in chalk. The finest example of brick building on the Wolds is the village of **Sledmere**.

DINOSAURS WALKED HERE

The most remarkable fossils on the Dinosaur Coast are not the remains of shellfish, nor the leaves of plants, nor the bones of reptiles. In fact they are not even the actual remains of organisms at all, simply a trace left in the rock by their passing. But the footprints of dinosaurs, clearly visible on the shore rocks at Burniston and Scalby, hold a powerful fascination. When we see the tracks of these strange and wonderful creatures we can almost feel their presence.

Dinosaurs lived on the Yorkshire coast in the Middle Jurassic period. At that time this was a warm, low-lying coastal area on the western margin of a great ocean known as the Tethys Sea. Over the period of millions of years that the dinosaurs flourished, sea levels rose and fell. For most of the time this was a land of deltas and sandbars, of silt brought in rivers from the landmass to the west, though occasionally it would be sub-merged by the sea. The dinosaurs thrived on the abundant plants that grew along the coast and, most important to us, they left their foot-prints in the sand and silt and mud of the beaches and deltas. Some of these foot-prints have, by good fortune, been preserved for over 160 million years.

Footprints most commonly survive as casts which stand above the surface of the surrounding rock. When the print is left in silt or fine sand, harder material is often washed in as the silt hardens. This infilling resists erosion and the cast of the print is preserved. These three-toed prints, each about 15 cm long, are from Wood End Museum in Scarborough.

Dinosaurs that lived here included species of theropod, which were carnivorous, and sauropod which were large plant-eaters. A wing bone of a pterosaur has also been found.

Most of the footprints at Burniston and Scalby Bays are three-toed (tridactyl) though there are a few five-toed (pentadactyl). They vary in size from 3 cm to over 50 cm, which means the largest dinosaurs here were over 2.5 metres at the hip – easily taller than a man. The hammer shows the size of these prints from Scalby Bay. They appear as hollows in the rock which get filled with loose sand.

PLACES TO GO

■ Dinosaur footprints have been found at **Saltwick** and **Burniston** but the best place to see them is at **Scalby Bay** (also known locally as Jackson's Bay). You can walk round from Scalby Mills or south from Burniston, but always go on a falling tide. Prints get weathered out of the surrounding rock and get worn away, so the locations change. It is very important not to damage any prints that you find – see Fossil Hunting on page 63.

■ A sandstone block containing thirteen footprints from several different dinosaur species is built into the 'reptile wall' at Whitby Museum. It was discovered at Saltwick in 1908. The Museum has other individual footprints on display.

■ Wood End Museum in Scarborough has individual footprints and photographic records of some prints that have been eroded.

Dinosaur footprints were first discovered on the Yorkshire coast in 1895 at Saltwick. In 1962 this trackway of nine prints (below) was found at Scalby. The prints (below) are 45 cm long and the length of stride is about 1.3 metres. The prints became more prominent as the sandstone was washed by the sea.

Dinosaur bones are extremely rare in this area. This foot bone of a sauropod is about 30 cm long and was found at Scarborough.

SCARBOROUGH CASTLE

Scarborough has the finest natural setting of any seaside resort in England. The land rises steeply from the sweep of the twin bays to the sloping plateau on which most of the town is built. This small plain is then ringed by the heights of Oliver's Mount to the south and the Tabular Hills to the west. And in the centre of this magnificent setting is Castle Hill. The headland on which the castle was built not only defended the town in times of trouble, it is the reason for the town's existence. And for this we have to thank a geological fault.

Castle Hill towers over the Old Town district of Scarborough and over both bays. From South Bay (above) it looks like a parallel-sided headland but the shape of the hill itself is more oval (left).

All the way along the Dinosaur Coast geological faults are responsible for putting rocks of different types and ages alongside each other. The resulting effects on the landscape vary from one fault to another. At Scarborough it seems that a major slip of land down a fault plane has given the headland its particular shape. Seen from above, Castle Hill has a narrow neck and a large body. The major fault caused hard young rocks of the Upper Jurassic period, known as calcareous grits, to appear on the surface. These have resisted erosion and caused the headland to stick out into the North Sea while the softer rocks around it have been worn away. This fault cuts right across the neck of the headland from north to south, crosses South Bay and reappears at Osgodby Point where it creates another headland.

On the north side the cliff face shows the geological fault. The clear diagonal slope from the building on the right hilltop is a fault that cuts off the thick beds of sandstone that lie below it. The rocks in the cliff face to the left of the fault are then softer and have been eroded by natural drainage and storms.

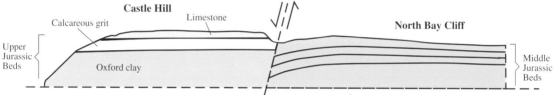

The fault is exposed on the north side of Castle Hill. The rocks are downthrown to the left on the section, bringing younger harder Upper Jurassic rocks next to the Middle Jurassic strata that outcrop to the north.

PLACES TO GO

■ You can see the outline of Castle Hill from both the **South Bay** and **North Bay** and you get an even better view from the top of **Oliver's Mount**.

■ Walk along **Marine Drive** on the north side until you can see the old footbridge. From here the fault in the cliffs is clearly visible.

■ While you are walking stop to look at the blocks of stone in the wall on the castle side of the road. You should be able to discover a variety of fossil shells including bivalves, oysters, razor-fish and sea-urchins.

■ You can appreciate the narrow neck of the headland by going to **St Mary's Church** and walking down the short road towards Rutland Terrace. The land falls steeply to the north and south and the high ground linking the castle to the town is only a matter of metres across.

The walls around the bottom of Castle Hill are built from blocks of stone that have fallen out of the cliff face. Lots of them contain fossils like these bivalves (left, above) and some are packed full of tiny shells (left). These are the remains of the millions of sea creatures that lived on this coast in the Upper Jurassic.

THE ROTUNDA

It is rare for a building to represent the architecture, the science, and the society of its time, and even more unusual for the same building to combine form and function, beauty and practicality. The Rotunda Museum at Scarborough does all of this. One of the oldest purpose-built museums in existence, it is a gem of a building and is of great historical and scientific importance. No visit to the Yorkshire coast is complete without a look inside the Rotunda.

In the 1820s the new science of geology was beginning to grasp the imaginations of educated people. There was a great interest in fossil collecting and in new theories about the history of the earth. Geology was the centre of great controversy because it seemed to show that the earth had been made over many thousands, if not millions, of years, whereas the Bible said the world was created in six days. The arguments increased interest in geology until it seemed that everyone had their own collection of fossils and minerals. The next step was for museums to be built to house these growing collections. Because of the coastline with its endless supply of fossils, Scarborough was a hot-bed of geology and was one of the first towns to build a museum. But the inspiration for the Rotunda came from one man — William Smith.

From the outside the Rotunda is as it was at its opening in 1829, except that two wings were added in 1860.

William Smith came to Scarborough for a two-year stay in 1824. Smith was a great pioneer of geology. His work on matching fossil types to particular rock strata laid the ground for the subject and he was the first to conceive and then produce a geological map. But in 1824 he was on his uppers. Smith had been travelling the north of England working as a surveyor for five years after spending time in a debtor's prison in London. At Scarborough he found a new home where he was greeted with enthusiasm by people eager to learn more about his work. He, in turn, had always wanted to build a museum. It was a perfect opportunity.

ELEVATION

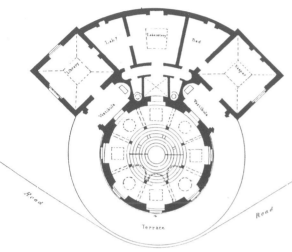

PLAN.

The architect Richard Sharp of York produced these drawings following William Smith's instructions. Smith had seen a rotunda in London and he asked Sharp to follow that design. The fossils and rocks were arranged in the order in which they occurred – the youngest in the cases at the top, the oldest at the bottom. The order around the walls reflected the order of rocks on the Yorkshire coast.

The interior and glass cases are as they were in 1829 when the building opened. The fossil collection was moved to Wood End Museum on The Crescent in the 1950s. A section of the rocks on the coast was drawn around the inside of the dome by John Phillips. He was the nephew of William Smith and went on to become Professor of Geology at Oxford and President of the Geological Society. Phillips' section is still there.

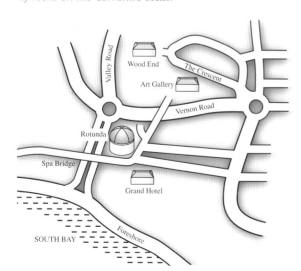

The Rotunda is on Valley Road just a few yards from the South Bay beach. Wood End Museum (above) is not far away, at the southern end of The Crescent – visit the next door art gallery while you are there. Both buildings, and the Crescent itself, are fine examples of early Victorian architecture.

CORAL SEA

YORKSHIRE IN THE UPPER JURASSIC

The sea invaded this area again in the Upper
Jurassic period, around 150 million years ago.
This was a warm, shallow sea with ammonites
and plesiosaurs. But most fossils from this time
are of animals living on the sea bed – sea
urchins, corals, gastropods, bivalves and crinoids.
The rocks of the Upper Jurassic are gritstones,
oolitic limestones and clays.

THE TABULAR HILLS

Running inland from Scarborough for about 30 miles is one of the most captivating landscapes in Britain. A range of flat-topped wooded and moor-land hills is cut by a series of deep green dales. To the south there are views over the Vale of Pickering to the distant chalk wolds and, to the north, a magnificent escarpment overlooking the southern slopes of the North York Moors. Geology, forestry and agriculture have combined to make the Tabular Hills a place of outstanding natural beauty.

The Hole of Horcum is cut into the plateau of the Tabular Hills by a series of springs. Just to the north the hills end at Saltergate Brow, giving a panoramic view of the central moorland.

Although they fall within the North York Moors National Park, the Tabular Hills are geologically distinct. They are made of younger rocks that once covered the whole of the region. These hard sandstones and lime-stones are being gradually eroded from the north, exposing the older rocks that lie underneath. To the south, the younger beds dip downwards, disappearing under the still younger sediments of the Vale of Pickering.

The rocks of the Tabular Hills were formed in a warm shallow sea with coral reefs and all have a high lime content. Sandstones at the base give way to a bed of limestone, known as the Hambleton Oolite, which runs along the top of the southern slope of the hills. These limey rocks produce more fertile soil. Moorlands give way to forests mixed with pasture and arable fields. The rocks slope away to the south and come up against a major geological fault running along the northern edge of the flat Vale of Pickering. This fault brings much younger clay up against the sandstones and limestones. Water flowing south through the porous rocks of the hills cannot penetrate the clay so it comes up to the surface in a series of springs. The villages along the A170 west from Brompton follow this fault and, of course, the line of springs. Rocks are not just for building stones and minerals – they also dictate where we live!

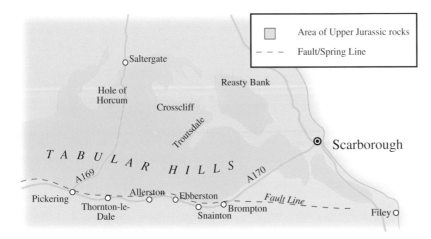

Area of Upper Jurassic rocks

– – – Fault/Spring Line

Saltergate

Reasty Bank

Hole of Horcum

Crossliff

Troutsdale

Scarborough

T A B U L A R   H I L L S

A169

A170

Pickering

Allerston

Ebberston

Fault Line

Thornton-le-Dale

Snainton

Brompton

Filey

Erosion by rainwater and drainage is an irregular business. While the Upper Jurassic rocks of the Tabular Hills are being remorselessly worn away from the north, a few pieces have remained. These 'outliers' are dotted around the moors, making a series of peculiar conical hills. This one is Blakey Topping, east of the Hole of Horcum.

Natural drainage from the uplands to the north is gradually eroding the Tabular Hills away. Because the hills are capped by hard rocks, the erosion creates steep slopes. The northern escarpment, seen here from Broxa, runs from east to west. The upper slopes, with their poor soils are used for forestry, the lower dalesides for pasture.

PLACES TO GO

■ There are lots of places to walk on the northern edge of the Tabular Hills with wonderful views. Try **Row Brow** west of Scarborough, **Reasty Bank** above Harwood Dale and **Crosscliff Brow** in Dalby Forest.

■ **Troutsdale** cuts a beautiful winding course through the hills, starting at Cockmoor Hall and ending at Hackness.

■ The **Hole of Horcum** is a well-known landmark. From here you can walk along **Saltergate Brow** and look over Fylingdales Moor to the north. For the energetic, a footpath links Crosscliff Brow to Saltergate.

■ You can see over the Vale of Pickering to the Wolds from the southern slope of Tabular Hills. Lanes and footpaths to the north of Brompton, Snainton and Ebberston give fine views.

■ **Blakey Topping**, **Howden Hill** at Langdale End and **Blea Hill** on Fylingdales Moor are all outliers from the Tabular Hills. Some Upper Jurassic rocks survive on the northern side of the Moors in the area just south of Scaling Dam reservoir. A hard cap of Corallian rock sits on top of the spectacular **Freeborough Hill**.

CAYTON BAY

South of Scarborough the Dinosaur Coast changes dramatically. The towering cliffs, small coves and rocky scars are replaced by a series of sweeping sandy bays. The high rock cliffs give way to low hills made of nothing more substantial than mud, as the beds of Jurassic rock slope southwards from the central arch of the moors and disappear under much younger sediments. But the landscape is not quite so simple as this. A series of geological faults cross the coast creating rocky headlands. The handsome arc of Cayton Bay is the result of two of these faults — one at either end.

The fault that passes through Scarborough's Castle Hill crosses the coast again at White Nab and goes through to Osgodby Point at the northwest end of Cayton Bay. Here sandstone forms the seaward part of the headland with an outcrop of mixed limestone and mudstone known as cornbrash on the inner side. The cliffs of the northern part of the bay itself are of clay which has been eroded back to form a strong curve.

We are now mostly seeing rocks formed in the Upper Jurassic period around 150 million years ago. There was a change from the delta landscape of the Middle Jurassic. Softer clays and sandstones were laid down as sea levels rose. Then harder limestones and gritty sandstones were deposited in warm shallow seas. The types of sea creatures living here changed as well and so the fossils are different. Ammonites continued to thrive but other marine animals became abundant. All these fossils were collected from local Upper Jurassic rocks.

Gastropod, close relation of modern winkles and snails (12 cm).

Colonial coral (35 x 25 cm).

The cliffs on the southeast side of Cayton Bay have a spectacular overhang. This is caused by a layer of hard calcareous grit over-laying a soft bed of clay. Further round at the end of the bay is the Red Cliff. Here a fault has a downthrow to the west, reversing the normal trend of faults. The fault can be clearly seen cutting through the headland (right).

Above, Starfish (25 cm).
Below right, Group of Trigonia bivalves (30 x 30cm).

PLACES TO GO

■ **Cayton Bay** is a magnet for summer holiday makers but it is a beautiful place at any time of year. As well as the headlands at either end, the cliffs and beach are full of interest. Near the steps the cliffs are mainly boulder clay brought here by ice sheets in the last ice age. The sea washes pebbles, and sometimes agates and semi-precious stones, out of the soft clay and dumps them on the beach. The pebbles often have no relation to the rocks in this region because they come from far away. The nearest granite is in Scotland, but granite pebbles are quite common! It is possible to trace ice sheet movements from, for example, Scandinavia.

White Nab

Cayton Bay is bordered by a fault at either end, at Osgodby Point and Red Cliff.

Osgodby Point

Cayton Bay

Red Cliff

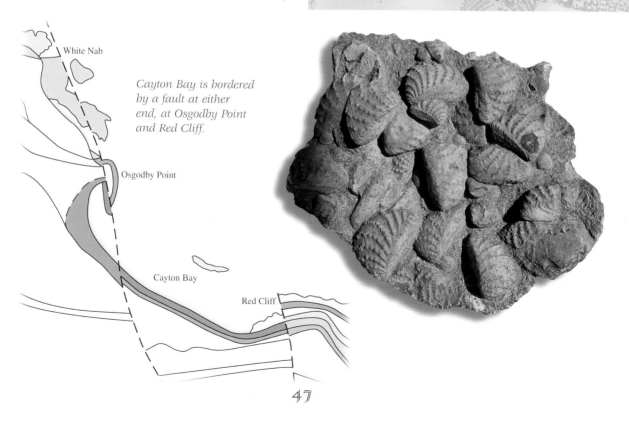

FILEY BRIGG

Shooting out into the North Sea like an arrow, Filey Brigg is one of the great landmarks of the Yorkshire coast. Such a strange landform is bound to attract legends and the Brigg has more than its share. Was the devil building a bridge across the waters so that witches could travel to and from Scandinavia? Even without tall tales, Filey Brigg is a magical place both when the waves crash over its northern face and when the tide is low enough to let you stand, seemingly in the middle of the sea.

Filey Brigg is, naturally enough, a product of erosion. The sea has worn away at the rocks of the coast for millions of years, creating bays, headlands and steep cliffs. At this point the sea meets an extremely hard slab of rock known as the Birdsall Calcareous Grit. At the particular time in the Upper Jurassic when the rocks around Filey were formed, this was a shallow warm sea. The rocks being deposited were oolitic limestones, easily recognised by their bead-like grains. At some point the southern side of this area of sea was slightly lifted and a great wedge of sand poured onto the sea floor. This has survived as the bed of hard calcareous grit, about 6 metres thick, that forms the Brigg.

Seen from the top of Carr Naze, the bed of hard grit that makes the Brigg dips to the south. Underlying the grit, visible on the north side is a bed of oolite. Great slabs of this oolite are broken off by the sea and thrown up onto the Brigg, forming a bank of boulders.

On the south side of the Brigg and Carr Naze the beds above the hard grit are exposed (above). The prominent bed of rock here is once again oolite, from a formation known as the Hambleton Oolite that runs along the top of the Tabular Hills. This bed contains lots of bivalves and occasional ammonites. Above it is a thick layer of soft glacial boulder clay that is being rapidly worn away by wind and rain.

On the north side of Carr Naze (left) the oolite has been carved by the sea into circular hollows in the cliffs called doodles.

The loose blocks at the landward end of the Brigg are made of oolitic limestone. Many of the blocks (above) contain these spectacular fossilised burrows known as Thalassinoides. The burrows made by the creature in the sea bed became filled with sand which was slightly harder than the surrounding material. When the sea washes these rocks it gradually wears away the softer stone leaving the burrows standing out. They are hard to miss – each burrow is as thick as a human finger.

PLACES TO GO

▪ You can get to **Filey Brigg** from above by driving to the country park and walking down. This gives splendid views over Filey Bay and south towards Flamborough.. Alternatively start at Filey sea front and walk round the base of the cliff. The Brigg is best seen at low water, so always go there on a falling tide.

▪ The fossil burrows are in boulders at the base of the Brigg. Look out for other fossils as you walk along the scar. There are lots of rockpools to look in too.

The rocks of the Brigg are rich in bivalves.

FILEY BAY and NORTH SEA OIL

Protected by the headland of Carr Naze and Filey Brigg to the north, Filey Bay is a glorious five-mile long sweep of sand. The bay also marks the boundary between two major geological periods. At Reighton Gap the youngest rocks of the Jurassic period make a brief appearance in the cliff. Going south towards Speeton these dip down and give way to beds of clay from the Cretaceous period. Further round the bay this Speeton Clay gives way in turn to the great beds of chalk that form the cliffs at Bempton and Flamborough. This boundary is of great interest to geologists because it is an exact copy of the rock formations under the neighbouring sea floor, and it is these rocks that are the source of North Sea oil.

The youngest and therefore highest rock of the Jurassic period is known as the Kimmeridge Clay. It is not seen on the surface in many places but it is a key rock formation. The clay lies beneath the modern lake sediments of the Vale of Pickering. Because the clay is impermeable to water it creates a spring line along the north side of the vale. As well as helping to bring water to the surface, the Kimmeridge Clay is a major source of oil. We know that dead marine animals fall to the sea floor

Filey Bay stretches for more than five miles and marks the boundary between the Jurassic and Cretaceous periods of the Earth's history.

continually and their shells are often preserved as fossils. But under certain conditions the organic matter of plants and animals is preserved as well. This can become converted into carbon-rich material which is eventually, over millions of years, changed into crude oil.

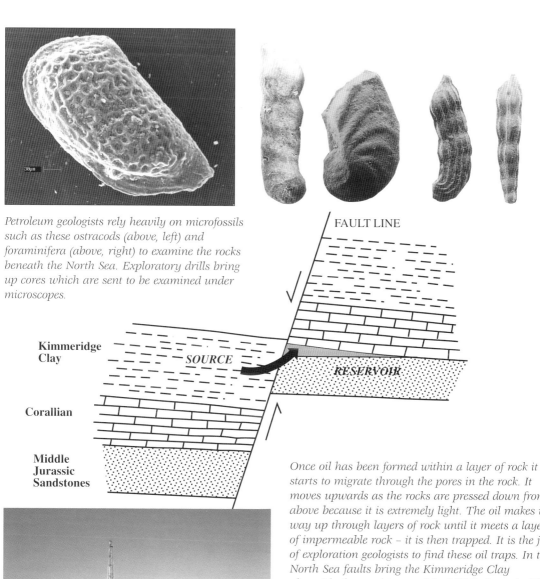

Petroleum geologists rely heavily on microfossils such as these ostracods (above, left) and foraminifera (above, right) to examine the rocks beneath the North Sea. Exploratory drills bring up cores which are sent to be examined under microscopes.

FAULT LINE

Kimmeridge Clay

SOURCE

RESERVOIR

Corallian

Middle Jurassic Sandstones

Once oil has been formed within a layer of rock it starts to migrate through the pores in the rock. It moves upwards as the rocks are pressed down from above because it is extremely light. The oil makes its way up through layers of rock until it meets a layer of impermeable rock – it is then trapped. It is the job of exploration geologists to find these oil traps. In the North Sea faults bring the Kimmeridge Clay alongside the sandstones of the Middle Jurassic. The oil migrates into these very porous rocks and a trap is then formed. Petroleum geologists study the Kimmeridge Clay around Filey because of the similarity with rock formations found under the North Sea.

Oil rigs in the North Sea drill down to reach the Middle Jurassic sandstones where oil from the Kimmeridge Clay has become trapped. Watery mud is pumped into the rock at high pressure. This forces the oil up and out through the pipe to the surface.

PLACES TO GO

■ At **Filey Brigg** the rocks are of Upper Jurassic age. Walk along the beach to the south and you will come to **Reighton Gap** (alternatively use the road and walk down to the beach at Reighton). Walk south from here and you cross the boundary from Jurassic to Cretaceous. This is more obvious the further you go as you begin to see chalk, the key rock of the Cretaceous period.

THE VALE OF PICKERING

The landscape of northeast Yorkshire is dominated by its uplands — the northern and central moorlands, the Tabular Hills, the Wolds, are all evidence of massive rock formations being lifted by forces active in the earth's crust. But lowlands have their stories too, and none is more interesting than the geological history of the Vale of Pickering, a great flat expanse circled by ranges of hills. Whereas most geology is to do with events that happened millions of years ago, this story is different, because, within the comparatively recent past, the Vale of Pickering was a lake.

The flat patchwork of fields on the floor of the Vale of Pickering is visible from the surrounding hills. The rocks beneath are a type of clay which is now covered by the mud that formed at the bottom of the lake. No expanse of land is entirely flat so the lake drained unevenly. Parts of the vale were under water in human history and most of it was marsh land just a few hundred years ago.

The extent of Lake Pickering varied over the thousands of years since the last ice age. At its largest it covered an area roughly 25 miles by 5 miles. The North Sea ice sheet penetrated inland as far as Wykeham and held up the eastern edge of the lake waters.

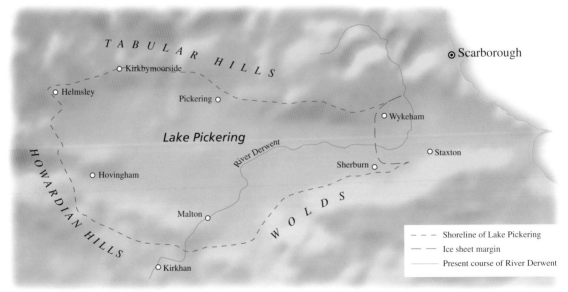

Lake Pickering was fed by waters draining off the North York Moors and Tabular Hills to the north. The landscape here has been marked by lakes and channels that existed alongside the ice sheets. Forge Valley near Scarborough (left) is an outflow channel from a glacial lake that stood at Hackness. The biggest outflow channel is Newtondale, a great gorge cut through the Tabular Hills by waters flowing from a lake in Eskdale down to Lake Pickering. Newtondale is the route of the North Yorkshire Moors steam railway.

Many visitors to the Dinosaur Coast cross the Vale of Pickering on the last part of their journey. By road or rail from York you find yourself on a flat stretch for about 8 miles. Then the countryside is hilly for 3 or 4 miles, until you pass Malton, where you enter another very flat plain — the Vale of Pickering. As you approach Scarborough you begin to see hills to the left and to the right gradually converging as the vale narrows. The vale is actually enclosed by hills on three sides; the Tabular Hills along its northern margin, the Wolds to the south and the Howardian Hills to the west. The eastern side of the vale is open because when the lake was first formed this was the edge of an ice sheet that covered the North Sea. Lake Pickering was one of a series of glacial lakes that were held in place by surrounding ice. The edge of the ice sheet is now marked by a bank of moraine — rubble carried by the leading edge of the sheet — that lies across the vale near the village of Wykeham.

The waters of Lake Pickering were held in place by ice sheets and the surrounding hills. But then, during the latter stages of the last ice age, the water began to find a way out of the lake just to the southwest of Malton. Once the water began to flow it quickly cut a steep-sided valley in the hills and flowed out from Lake Pickering into the Vale of York. This valley is known to geologists as the Kirkham Gorge or Gap and is now the course of the River Derwent (above). In fact the reason the Derwent flows away from the coast instead of into the North Sea is because of Lake Pickering.

PLACES TO GO

■ From the top of **Staxton Hill** on the Wolds there is a wonderful view of the eastern end of the Vale of Pickering, with Oliver's Mount and Forge Valley clearly visible.

■ Walk along any of the paths and minor roads that cross the Vale of Pickering and you will see drainage ditches everywhere. These are used to turn marshes into land suitable for farming.

■ Take the train from Scarborough to York. When you leave Malton station, notice how the land begins to rise on either side of the track. Soon you are following the River Derwent through a steep valley, past the ruins of **Kirkham Abbey**. This valley is where the waters of Lake Pickering drained out.

■ **Forge Valley** is a beautiful place to visit. This deep valley was cut by glacial waters from Hackness draining to Lake Pickering.

OLIVER'S MOUNT and the MERE

Just south of Scarborough a huge escarpment rises out of the coastal plateau. Oliver's Mount rises to 150 metres and towers over the southern part of the town. The hill is actually the most easterly part of the Tabular Hills that run almost uninterrupted to Helmsley in the west. The connection of Oliver's Mount with the rest of the range is not obvious because a large valley has been carved through the hills separating the mount from the rest. All of Scarborough's links with the south and the west run through this peculiar riverless valley.

In common with the other Tabular Hills, Oliver's Mount has a hard cap of gritty sandstone formed in the Upper Jurassic period. This thick bed of grit (known as the Lower Calcareous Grit) lies on top of a bed of Oxford Clay. The clay is softer and erosion by rainwater produces steep sides on the north, west and east of the mount. To the south the hill slopes down much more gently as the beds of grit dip

Seen from Falsgrave Moor, Oliver's Mount is on the same level. The northern end, where the memorial and mast are, is a sharp escarpment. A level area in the centre, now used for football pitches, slopes off gradually to the south.

naturally in that direction. The mount is shaped like a boat's prow with the bow rising up out of the surrounding coastal plateau.

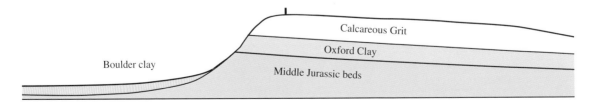

Calcareous Grit

Oxford Clay

Boulder clay

Middle Jurassic beds

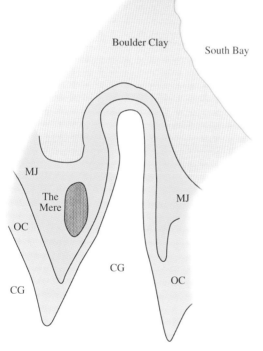

Boulder Clay

South Bay

MJ

The Mere

MJ

OC

CG

OC

CG

Scarborough's Mere is one of a handful of natural lakes in Yorkshire. It lies in the valley between Oliver's Mount and the Tabular Hills. The valley was probably cut by meltwater during one of the warmer periods in the Pleistocene ice ages. In the most recent glaciation, the valley may well have filled with ice. When this retreated banks of mud were left behind and these have blocked the previous water course, creating a natural lake.

PLACES TO GO

■ A trip to the top of **Oliver's Mount** is a must for any visitor to Scarborough. The views over the South Bay and harbour are magnificent.
■ The long western flank of the mount is clearly visible from the A64 Seamer Road, while the eastern side is tracked by Filey Road.
■ From the top of the hill at **Falsgrave Moor** you get a good impression of Oliver's Mount being a continuation of the hills to the west.

On a geological map Oliver's Mount stands isolated in a sea of surrounding glacial mud. The contrast between the bed of Lower Calcareous Grit on top and the Oxford Clay beneath is what makes the mount. The softer rocks that underlie it are visible only on the sloping sides. As the beds of rock taper off to the south, the glacial deposits eventually overlie the grit just north of Eastfield. The valley that carries the York to Scarborough railway line and the main A64 road stands out starkly on the map. Glacial mud in the valley bottom shows that there was a lobe of ice in the valley in the last glaciation, but the valley was created before that, probably by meltwater from a previous ice sheet.

FLAMBOROUGH and the WOLDS

From Filey Bay southwards the nature of the Yorkshire coast changes again. From here to the grand headland at Flamborough there are high vertical cliffs — and after that, no more cliffs until Kent. The greater part of the seaboard of eastern England is made of chalk. At Flamborough and on the Yorkshire Wolds the chalk stands high, forming cliffs and uplands, further south it sinks beneath a thick layer of boulder clay brought by ice sheets. The chalk produces its own landscape and is the product of a different world from the rocks further north.

At some time in the Cretaceous period of the earth's history, around 140 to 65 million years ago, much of the earth's surface was under sea water. This was probably because the temperature became warm enough to melt the polar ice sheets, leading to a rise in sea levels. Many areas that had been on the margins of continents were flooded and became warm shelf seas, rather like the Caribbean today. In these waters lived countless millions of minute plants and animals, in particular coccoliths and foraminifera. When they died they fell to

The chalk at Flamborough has been carved into a series of spectacular arches and stacks by the sea. Though normally regarded as a soft rock, the chalk at Flamborough itself is hard enough to have been used occasionally as a building stone.

the sea floor where they eventually became pressurised by more and more piling on top, until they solidified into rock. Chalk is made up of the remains of these animals which are almost pure calcium carbonate.

Sponge (28 cm long)

Sponge
(9 cm across)

The fossils of the Cretaceous chalk are quite different from those of the Jurassic rocks to the north. These are creatures that thrived in warm, clear, shallow seas and lagoons. These fossils from Scarborough's Wood End Museum are sponges (above, left and right), a beautifully preserved echinoid (below, right) and a shark's tooth (below, left).

Echinoid (4 cm)

Shark tooth
(3.5 cm)

PLACES TO GO

■ **Flamborough Head** is visible from lots of places on the coast. You can see the chalk cliffs close up at **Selwicks Bay** and at **North Landing** at Flamborough.
■ The RSPB reserve at **Bempton** takes in a magnificent stretch of chalk cliffs. You get great views of the cliffs and stacks, as well as the sea birds, from the cliff-top path.
■ Boat trips run from **Bridlington** up the coast past Flamborough to Bempton.
■ The **Wolds** offer a marvellous chalk landscape. Almost everywhere you will see open hills and dry valleys.

The outcrop of chalk swings inland from Flamborough to form the upland area known as the Yorkshire Wolds. This is a characteristic chalk land-scape. The rock is very porous so there is little surface water and few trees. The hills and valleys are rounded. Dig in to the Wolds and you find chalk – as here in a roadside quarry near Langtoft. Notice that the beds on the left are dipping steeply down to the right, while those on the right are more horizontal.

THE CHANGING COAST

The making of the landscape of the Dinosaur Coast has been going on for millions of years. Some of the processes, like the formation of rock from sand deposited at the bottom of the sea, are extremely slow. But others are surprisingly fast. The rocks of the coast bear evidence of landslips, underwater slumps and other changes that happened millions of years ago but took only a matter of days to have their effect. And these changes have not stopped. The sea is still battering away the coastline while sand is being brought by rain and rivers and laid on the sea bed. Geology goes on working.

We tend to think of erosion as a slow and steady process but it is much more likely to appear as periods of calm punctuated by sudden activity. The bases of cliffs are worn away with every tide but it is only when a critical imbalance is reached that there will be a sudden collapse of rocks from above. Water infiltrates porous clays and muds over many years and then a bank or hillside will suddenly give way. We see this happening all the time today, though some examples are more spectacular than others.

Cliff collapse led to the temporary disappearance of the Cleveland Way footpath above Port Mulgrave (left). Coastal erosion is inevitable and there is a lively debate over whether defences are worthwhile. Shoreline boulders used at Scarborough and Whitby protect the foot of the cliff but they increase wave activity beneath the water line. Many of us are drawn to the coast because of the sense of wildness and energy that the sea possesses. We have to learn to live with the effects of the sea's power.

The east coast of Britain has been moving westwards for thousands of years, changing shape as it is worn away by the sea. But the sea is not the only agent of erosion. In the spring of 1993 rain water soaked steadily in to the mud cliffs on Scarborough's South Bay. The water made the cliff unstable and, on 3rd June 1993, a section of the wet mud began to slip over its rock base down towards the sea. This was a natural readjustment of the landform but, unfortunately, the mud took half of the Holbeck Hall Hotel (above and left) with it. Guests had to hurriedly leave the dining room, but the disintegration of the building went on for several days – avidly watched by the nation on television. This was earth science in action! The mud slide has now been grassed over and the base is protected from the sea by a ring of boulders.

This rock is in cliffs in the centre of Cayton Bay. The cliffs are made of soft boulder clay brought by ice sheets. This boulder carries clear scratch lines or striations made by the movement of the ice. From Scarborough south, cliffs made from soft boulder clay and mud become more common and erosion is much more rapid. On the Holderness coast south of Bridlington the land is disappearing at an average rate of 2.4 metres per year.

PLACES TO GO

■ You can see erosion going on everywhere on the Dinosaur Coast. The piles of rock on the scars and beaches have fallen out of the cliff faces.

■ The wave-cut platform at **Robin Hood's Bay**, visible at low tide, has been created by the action of the sea on the rock strata.

■ The cliffs in the centre of **Cayton Bay** are boulder clay = a soft mud full of fragments of rock. These stones get washed out of the cliff by the sea and end up as pebbles on the beach.

■ Walk from **Filey** round the beach to the Brigg, and look up at the cliffs at the north end of the bay. They are made of soft red mud and are marked by channels where rain water has washed the mud away. These cliffs are worn away by the sea from below and by rain from above.

ROCKS and LANDSCAPE

The Dinosaur Coast is the product of a long and fascinating history. On this part of the coast rocks of the Jurassic period are there for all to see, exposed in a series of spectacular cliffs and bays. This continuous exposure of rock has brought geologists flocking to the coast for generations. It was here, in the early days of geology, that many of the secrets of the earth's history were discovered.

In this guide we have looked at particular places and topics. The sketch below sets these in the context of the landscape of the region. The rocks tend to become younger as we go from north to south down the coast because the beds slope or dip towards the south. At Robin Hood's Bay the rocks are lifted up into a slight but significant arch which runs inland all the way to Ingleby Greenhow — this is the spine of the North

Yorkshire Wolds
Rolling low hills with dry valleys and few trees. A classic chalk landscape.

Vale of Pickering
Soft mudstones which overlay the south-sloping rocks of the Tabular Hills have been eroded down almost to sea level. This flat plain was a lake during and after the last ice age.

Tabular Hills
Range of hills stretching from Filey Brigg to Helmsley. Upper Jurassic hard sandstones lie on top of softer mudstone. Erosion from the north has created a steep and spectacular escarpment while the rock beds dip naturally down the long south-facing slope.

North York Moors
Hard sandstone of the Middle Jurassic sits on top of the central arch of the moors. Inland dales run north and south from the spine, cutting down into the softer Lower Jurassic shale underneath.

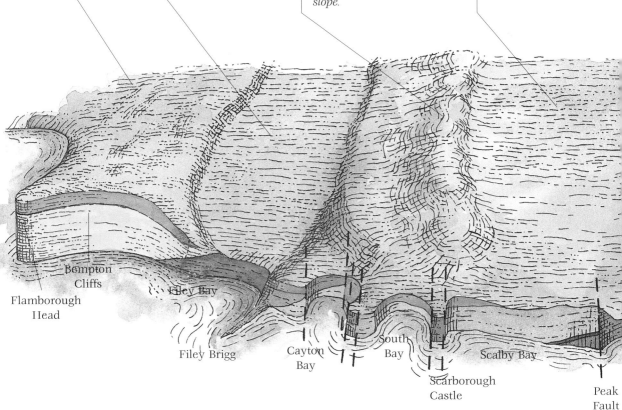

Flamborough Head

Bempton Cliffs

Filey Bay

Filey Brigg

Cayton Bay

South Bay

Scarborough Castle

Scalby Bay

Peak Fault

York Moors. This lifting brings the older Lower Jurassic rocks to the surface again in the hillsides around the bay. But then a major fault at Ravenscar has pushed the older rocks down, and from here southwards only rocks of Middle Jurassic age and younger are seen. The rock bed known as the Dogger is shown because it marks the boundary between Lower and Middle Jurassic rocks. South from Scarborough Castle a series of faults pushes rocks of the Middle and Upper Jurassic next to each other creating headlands and bays. At Filey Bay the Jurassic rocks dip under a sequence of clay beds from the lower part of the Cretaceous period. These clays in their turn dip away and are overlain by chalk from the Upper Cretaceous. The chalk formation is immensely thick and runs all the way to Flamborough and beyond. Many of these rocks are covered by mud and boulder clay dumped by retreating ice sheets. This section shows glacial mud only where it has been mentioned in this guide. The sketch shows how the landscape of the region reflects the rocks seen at the coast. The vertical scale is exaggerated to show the cliffs more clearly.

Eskdale

The upper part was a lake in the last ice age. Follows a fault line to meet the sea at Whitby.

Cleveland Hills

Hard sandstones of the Middle Jurassic provide the cap for these hills. Erosion from the north has created a steep escarpment. Lower Jurassic rocks are exposed on the northern side.

Glacial mud and boulder clay

Hard chalk (Upper Cretaceous)

Soft mudstone (Late Upper Jurassic and Lower Cretaceous)

Hard limestone and sandstone overlying soft clay (Early Upper Jurassic)

Hard sandstone and soft mudstone in layers (Middle Jurassic)

Dogger

Soft shales and mudstones (Lower Jurassic)

Geological Fault

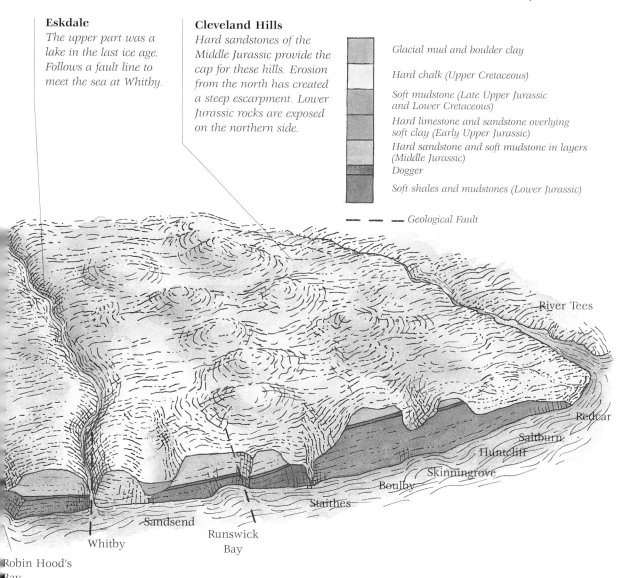

River Tees

Redcar

Saltburn

Huntcliff

Skinningrove

Boulby

Staithes

Sandsend

Runswick Bay

Whitby

Robin Hood's Bay

INFORMATION

USEFUL ORGANISATIONS AND ADDRESSES

The Yorkshire Dinosaur Coast Project is based at the Wood End Museum, The Crescent, Scarborough. Visit the website (www.dinocoast.org.uk) for information about the Dinosaur Coast and coming events, or call one of the tourist offices listed here and ask for a leaflet.

Whitby Museum in Pannett Park has a wonderful display of fossils including marine reptiles and giant ammonites.
Tel 01947 602908 www.whitby-museum.org.uk

The Tom Leonard Mining Museum at Skinningrove offers a trip round an ironstone mine and a fascinating insight into the iron mining industry.
Tel 01287 642877 www.ironstonemuseum.co.uk

The North York Moors National Park has visitor centres at Danby, Sutton Bank and Robin Hood's Bay.
Tel 01947 885900 for Robin Hood's Bay
www.northyorkmoors-npa.gov.uk

Scarborough Tourist Information.
Tel 01723 373333

Whitby Tourist Information.
Tel 01947 602674

Filey Tourist Information.
Tel 01723 512204

Bridlington Tourist Information.
Tel 01262 673474

FURTHER READING

There are lots of leaflets about the coast, its fossils, rocks, landscape, wildlife and industries available from the information centres and museums. For more background try the following books.
Geology of the North York Moors by Alan Staniforth, published by North York Moors National Park.

The Floating Egg by Roger Osborne, published by Pimlico.
The Yorkshire Coast by Peter Rawson and John Wright, published by the Geologists' Association.
North York Moors by Ian Sampson and Ian Carstairs, published by Pevensey Guides.

ACKNOWLEDGEMENTS

The authors have benefited from the expertise and advice of many people during the preparation of this book. In particular we would like to thank Alan Forster, John Rees, James Riding and Ian Wilkinson of the British Geological Survey, Helen Morgans of Oxford University, Kate Brennan of the Tom Leonard Mining Museum, Lynne Leitch of Shell Exploration and Peter Robinson.

PICTURE CREDITS

The Jurassic reconstructions on pages 8-9, 28-29 and 42-43 are by Robert Nicholls. Photograph credits: Tony Bartholomew pages 12, 13, 17, 23 (right), 25 (except top), 36, 37 (bottom), 38 (top), 39, 40, 41, 46, 47, 48, 49, 50, 54, 55, 57 (middle and top). Tom Leonard Mining Museum page 15. Whitby Museum page 18, 19. John Tindale page 24. Shell Exploration, by kind permission, page 51. Alan Forster, Jim Evans, James Riding and Ian Wilkinson, by kind permission, pages 51 (top), 58, 59: IPR/18-8C British Geological Survey. © NERC. All rights reserved. Peter Robinson, by kind permission, page 37 (middle). Michael Jaconelli, by kind permission, page 21. Roger Osborne pages 16, 20, 23 (left), 31, 34, 35 (top), 53 (bottom), 57 (bottom). Ryedale Council Tourism Department, by kind permission, page 52. The geological maps are based on British Geological Survey 1:50 000 Provisional Series, Sheets 34, 35, 44, 54. All other photographs supplied by North York Moors National Park Information Service and the Dinosaur Coast Project. Copyright in these photographs remains with the above organisations and individuals. We have made every effort to contact all copyright holders. If we have unwittingly misused anyone's copyright please accept our apologies and contact the publisher.

FOSSIL HUNTING

Fossil hunting is fun and a great way to learn about the history of life on earth, but you need to follow some basic guidelines. It is important that we do not damage our natural heritage in our eagerness to learn. Here are some points to remember.

RESPONSIBLE FOSSIL HUNTING
- Look for fossils in loose beach material
- Only collect a small number of fossils
- Keep detailed records (what, where and when)
- Keep hammering to a minimum
- Avoid disturbance to wildlife

SAFE FOSSIL HUNTING
- Check local tide tables
- Stay well away from the base of steep cliffs
- Let someone know where you are and what time you will return
- Wear appropriate footwear and clothing